What Damian Didn't Know About Dinosaurs

Carrie Weston
Illustrated by Louise Ellis

RIGBY

Daisy's big brother Damian reads lots of books. He thinks he knows everything about everything. But the thing Damian knows most about is dinosaurs.

Damian's bedroom is full of dinosaurs.

He has dinosaur posters, dinosaur models, a dinosaur duvet and . . . a big Pterodactyl hanging from the ceiling!

Damian says Daisy doesn't read enough books.
That's because Daisy loves to be outside, climbing
trees, building camps and making mud pies.

4

Berry/mud

One day, it was raining, and Daisy was bored. She crept into Damian's room and sat down on his bed. Damian looked up.

"Mum!" he shrieked, "Daisy's put dirt on the Diplodocus!"

"Which one is the Diplodocus?" asked Daisy.

"Don't you know anything?" said Damian rudely.

Compsognathus

7

Mum appeared at the door.

"Now, now," she said. "Why don't you tell Daisy something interesting about dinosaurs?"

"Yes, please!" said Daisy. There were lots of things she wanted to know.

9

"Which dinosaur was the **biggest**?" asked Daisy.
Damian rolled his eyes.

"That's so easy," he said. "It was the Seismosaurus
and it was up to 52 metres long. Next question."

"Which was the **smallest**?" asked Daisy.

"The Compsognathus was about the size of a chicken," said Damian rather proudly. "Next."

Daisy thought for a moment. She looked at a poster on the wall. It was a Tyrannosaurus rex. It had big teeth and sharp claws.

"Did dinosaurs ever get toothache?" she asked.

Damian scowled.

"I don't know," he said. "That's a silly question."

"How long were a Tyrannosaurus rex's claws?" asked Daisy. "Did they ever need to be cut?"

"How should I know?" said Damian.

Compsognathus

"Which dinosaur had the biggest feet?" went on
Daisy. "Did dinosaurs ever wash? What did they have
for breakfast?"

"I don't know," said Damian crossly. "Why don't you
look in a book?"

Daisy chose the biggest book on Damian's shelf.
She turned the pages and looked at the pictures.

"Did this one ever get neck ache?" she asked.

"How big was this dinosaur's brain?"

"How big was this dinosaur's dung?
Did this one ever get a runny nose?
Did they have bogies?
Did . . . "

Daisy was very excited about dinosaurs.

She didn't hear the door open.

"Did mummy dinosaurs have noisy children?" asked
Mum.

"Damian doesn't know everything about dinosaurs after all!" said Daisy.

Damian looked very grumpy.

"And neither do I," added Daisy.

Mum smiled.

"It will be the school holidays soon," she said.
"Who would like to go to the museum?"

"Me! **Me! Me!**" said Damian and Daisy together.

"Then we can find out all about dinosaurs," said
Daisy.

And that is what they did.

What Daisy and Damian found out about dinosaurs:

Dinosaur teeth

The *Tyrannosaurus rex* had 60 sharp, pointed, bone-crushing teeth – and strong jaws too! *Pelecanimimus* had over 220 sharp teeth!

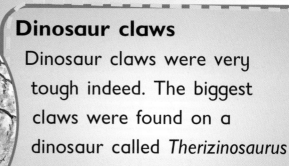

Dinosaur claws

Dinosaur claws were very tough indeed. The biggest claws were found on a dinosaur called *Therizinosaurus cheloniformis*. This dinosaur had curved claws up to 90 cm long!

Dinosaur feet

Many dinosaur footprints have been found. The biggest footprints ever found were those of a dinosaur known as *Breviparopus*.

Dinosaur brains

Dinosaurs did not have very big brains. The *Stegosaurus* was a huge creature but its brain was smaller than a peach!

Dinosaur dung

Scientists sometimes find remains of dinosaur dung! Meat-eating dinosaurs left lots of bones in their dung. Plant-eaters' dung was a bit like horse manure. The largest dinosaurs would have made huge piles of dung — luckily there were no people around to tread in it!

Dinosaur colds

No one has found any evidence to show that dinosaurs got colds — no fossilized bogies! But there is one theory that a virus, like a cold, caused dinosaurs to become extinct!

Dinosaur necks

The *Sauropods* had very long necks. They didn't get neck ache because their backbones were hollow. This made them light, but very strong!

Dinosaur families

Most dinosaurs laid eggs. Some dinosaurs left their babies to hatch out and survive on their own. This means that baby dinosaurs would not have made much noise. It was best to keep quiet in case you got eaten!